Contents

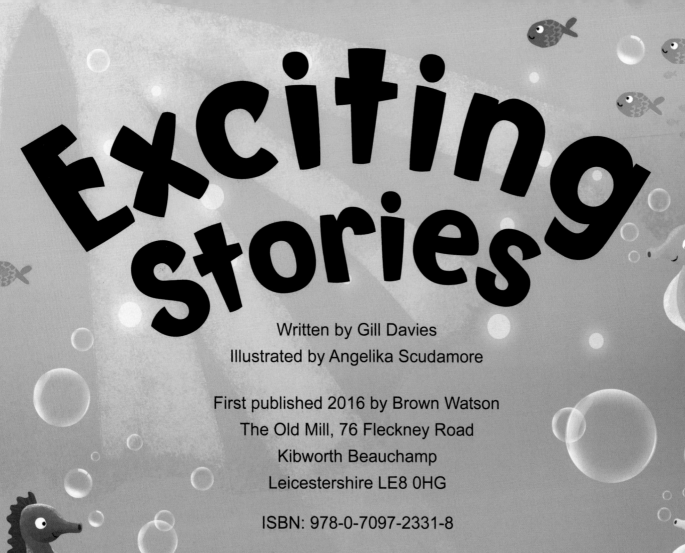

Exciting Stories

Written by Gill Davies

Illustrated by Angelika Scudamore

First published 2016 by Brown Watson

The Old Mill, 76 Fleckney Road

Kibworth Beauchamp

Leicestershire LE8 0HG

ISBN: 978-0-7097-2331-8

Printed in Malaysia

Brown Watson

ENGLAND

Planet Jolly

Astronaut Luke and his dog Barker were zooming very fast through
a deep purple sky. Their rocket flew past the Candy Floss moon
and whizzed away even higher than the blue planet,
Ice Pop. "This is so exciting," laughed Luke.
"Woof!" barked Barker.
"We are nearly there," cried Luke as he spotted the red planet,
Gum in the distance … but the rocket flew straight past Gum
and carried on into deep space.
"What is happening?" shouted Luke, "Stop, Rocket, stop!"
"Woof," barked Barker, "Woof! Woof!"

The rocket made a loud spluttering noise, began to slow and then landed on Planet Jolly. All the Jolly Jelly aliens came running up. "Welcome!" chuckled Pink Smiler.

"We sent our sticky space rays to pull you down here," laughed Orange Grin. "We wanted you to stay for a little holiday," giggled Purple Beamer. "Woof," barked Barker, "Woof! Woof! Woof!"

Luke and Barker had a wonderful time. They loved the wobbling jelly buildings and the Wibble Wobble Forests where all the trees shook with laughter.
But at last it was time to go.
"Goodbye," said Luke, a little sad.
"Travel safely!" cried Jolly Jellies, "Come back again soon!"
"We will," said Luke, smiling again.
"Woof," barked Barker, "Woof! Woof! Woof! Woof!"
Then off they flew back home.

Don't worry, Jimmy Jet!

Jimmy Jet had just started school, but had not made any friends. The bully jumbo boys laughed because he was bad at counting and couldn't say which colours were which, especially when everyone was staring at him.

"Don't worry," said his mother, "We'll soon sort all that out. Let's have a quick flying lesson and learn about counting and colours at the same time. Follow me."

11

Soon they were up in the sky, which was, Jimmy knew, bright blue.
"Now what colour are the clouds?" asked Mum.
"White," answered Jimmy. "I know everything once I am up here."
"How many can you count?" Mum asked next.
"One, two, three high up… four, five, six below, and three little ones;
so that is … seven, eight, nine."
"Perfect!" said Mum, "There really is no problem."

They reached an amazing rainbow and Jimmy knew exactly which stripes were red, yellow, pink, blue, purple, orange and green. His mother smiled. "Jimmy, you really are a clever little jet. Now next time anyone teases you or the teacher is waiting for an answer, just think of this rainbow. Stop worrying. Then you'll be fine."

Mum was right. Jimmy stopped being frightened. And then, not only did he know all (well, most) of the answers, but he was happy and laughing all the time, so he made lots of friends too.

A Whale of a Time

One very stormy day Gail the Whale and Olga Octopus were playing hide and seek. Gail was hiding deep down on the sea bottom, below a little boat that was tossing about on the waves. Olga Octopus could not spot her friend anywhere.

"Coming to get you," shouted Olga, spinning around, but the wind howled and snatched her voice away. Then, suddenly, a huge wave crashed down and the little boat turned upside down.

Straight away Gail the Whale rose to the surface to see what had happened. One very frightened boy, who had been tossed into the wild sea, was clinging onto a broken piece of wood.

"There's another little boy over here," squawked a keen-eyed seagull.

"And a poor girl bobbing about by me," shouted Olga Octopus.

In no time at all the children had been rounded up and clambered onto Gail's back. They were soaking wet but safe.

It was a wonderful ride home. The children were amazed to
find themselves whizzing along on top of a whale.
"No-one at school is going to believe this!" laughed Jack.
"When Miss Brown asks us what we did on our holidays, I know
what I'm going to write about," giggled Melanie.
"But I bet she won't believe you either!" said Joe, as Gail dropped
them all off by the harbour steps, safely back on dry land.

The Shy Sad Ogre

When you have no friends, it is very easy to feel cross all the time. And when you feel cross all the time, it is very difficult to make friends. Now the big green Ogre wanted to play but somehow his voice came out as a growl, so the children always ran away. When a football flew into his garden, the boys were far too scared to ask for it back. "No-one wants to play with me," sighed the shy sad Ogre.

The children wanted to put on a concert but they needed a theatre. "That big green ogre has one in his castle," said the postman. Everyone signed a petition to say how much they needed his help and then one brave little girl said, "I shall go and ask him." Unfortunately, the Ogre, who couldn't read, wasn't sure what to do with the petition, so instead he gobbled it up!

But he suddenly realised what he'd done and sobbed, "Please be friends with me. No-one ever comes to play here." The brave little girl gave him a hug and explained how they needed his help. How pleased the ogre was to let them share his theatre – and his garden. At last the castle was full of music and children and he was SO happy! The brave little girl taught him to read, so now big green CROSS Ogre is big green HAPPY Ogre.

Noisy Pirate Pip

Pip Pirate was very noisy. He was always singing LOUDLY or stamping or clattering plates. He fell over. He dropped the saucepans. He made the parrot squawk. "Be quiet, please," the other pirates begged. "Stop banging about!" complained the Captain. But Pip Pirate couldn't help himself.

Then one day, although the captain had groaned, "Ooooh! I have a terrible headache!" Pip fired eight booming cannonballs. This was the last straw. "I shall lock you up!" said Captain Crow.

So Pip found himself down in the deepest, darkest part of the boat. Two days later, however, Silly Sam left the hatch open when he came to fetch his rum from the stores. Pip slipped out. He was just about to jump into a dinghy and sail off, when a giant octopus rose out of the sea and began pulling the ship down below the waves.
"Boooo!" shouted Pip in his LOUDEST EVER voice. "BOOOO!"
The octopus was so surprised he raced away.

"You saved the ship, me boy!" cried the Captain.
"Three cheers for Pip!" shouted all the pirates.
Pip was so pleased to be free again that he promised to be as quiet as he possibly could from now on.Captain Crow let him sleep in the best cabin as a reward and because there were lots of books to read in there, Pip was a good deal quieter – most of the time, anyway.

Blunder's Bungle

Young Blunder is always making magic mistakes. None of his spells seem to work properly. Today the wizard has been trying to make his toy soldier Henry march along singing, but Henry keeps falling over and now he has twisted his leg. "My leg hurts. I am fed up – and lonely," sighs Henry. "Can't you magic me some friends?"

"I can try," mutters Blunder.

So Blunder raises his wand …
To his amazement, the room
is suddenly full of happy
marching soldiers – and more
keep coming in through the
window.

Henry is in fine form, strutting along in front, with no sign
of an injured leg, but Blunder can't seem to stop the spell.

There are soldiers everywhere, knocking over all the other toys, singing marching songs, banging drums and making so much noise that Blunder has a headache.

Meanwhile, Henry is thrilled to have so many fine new friends. Before long he has sorted them all out and restored order. All the little soldiers are marching smartly round the room in a neat line. Blunder, his headache now gone, peers around the door to watch as Henry leads ever more soldiers across the room, down the stairs and into the moonlit garden. Blunder has no idea how to stop more soldiers arriving. Magic spells can be so full of surprises!

Neat and Tidy

One bright moonlit night, George wakes up suddenly when his red ball bounces onto the bed and hits him on the nose. He rubs his eyes, amazed to see his toy crane rushing around, scooping up all the toys. "Whatever is happening?" cries George.

"Put me down," yells Robot.

"Crane is trying to tidy up," laughs Dino.

"But we like being in a mess!" cries Robot.

"Sorry," says Crane, popping Robot down, "But it is my New Year's Resolution to tidy up every night." And off he rushes again.
George stares, astonished to see all the toys being whizzed away into boxes, drawers and cupboards. At last only the jigsaw remains.
"Leave that," says Robot, "I do so love putting in the last piece."
"Fine," yawns Crane, "Anyway, I am tired now." Soon he is fast asleep in the bottom drawer.

The next day George's mother is amazed. "How have you managed to make your room so neat and tidy?" she asks, as they eat breakfast, "It was such a pickle when you went to bed last night." Upstairs, naughty grinning Robot says, "Crane is still snoring in the drawer. Let's get in a mess again, just to annoy him!" So out pop toys from every cupboard and box, giggling as they wait for Crane to wake or George to return.

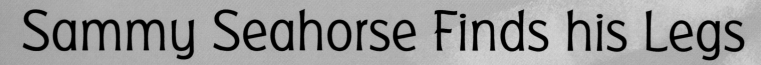

Sammy Seahorse Finds his Legs

Once there was a seahorse called Sammy who longed to have real legs and to be able to gallop. He would pretend that he was a racing horse, swimming as fast as he could, making crabs and starfish scuttle out of his way.

One day Neptune the Seaking announced, "Sammy, I shall grant your wish. Just for one day you shall gallop on the land."

He raised his trident. There was a bright flash of light as a knight in armour landed on Sammy's back.

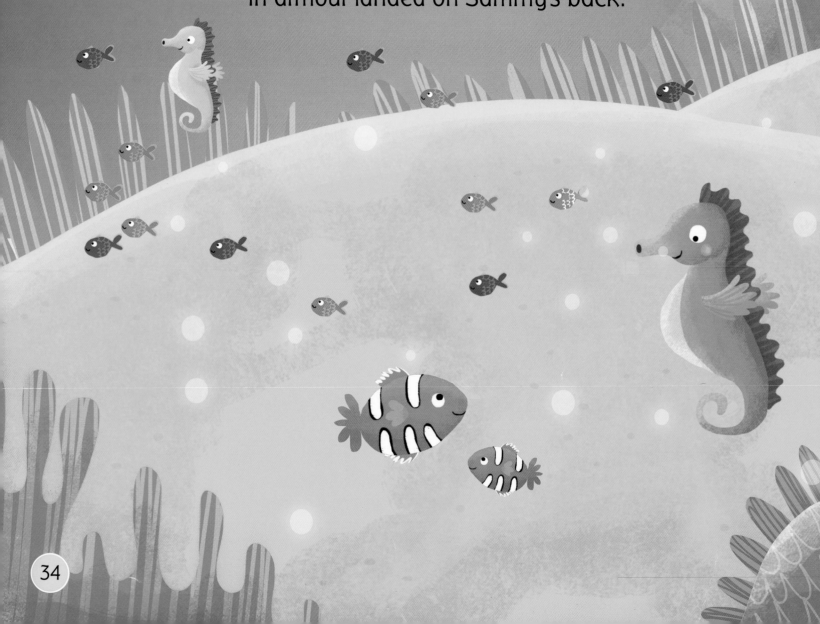

Up Sammy rose, right out of the ocean, and then found himself racing along a beach. Now he had real legs and a beautiful brown glossy coat. The knight clung onto his mane as Sammy's neat hooves thundered along below. Soon Sammy heard the sound of cheers and shouting. Then he rounded a bend – and there in front of him was a party of knights, on their way to a tournament.

"Do join us," they called.

Sammy had a wonderful time. He charged and raced. He neighed and snorted, thrilled to feel the sunshine on his velvety nose. At last it was time to go. Far away he could hear Neptune calling so he said farewell to all his fine new friends and galloped back into the sea. "I had an amazing day," he told the fish, as once again he bobbed about below the waves, "It was the best adventure ever."

Fireman Pete's Busy Day

One day when the children were playing in
the park, they were very surprised to see a
fire engine arriving, with its lights flashing.
Fireman Pete climbed out. "Someone told us
there was a fire here," he said.
"There must be some mistake."
"The park keeper was burning some
old leaves," said Joy.
"There was a lot of smoke – but no fire."
"Thanks for coming anyway," said Andy.
"Hey, that's a brilliant fire engine.
Can we see inside?"

"Of course!" said Fireman Pete, "Take a look." So the excited children all clambered aboard. Just then there was a loud miaowing noise from the top of the tree. "There's a kitten stuck up there!" cried Oliver. "Well, as we are here, we can certainly help," said Pete, opening up the ladder. He rescued the kitten in no time – and Joy's toy helicopter stuck in the branches.

Fireman Pete drove back to the fire station, but soon he and his other fireman friends were called out to deal with a house fire. Smoke and flames billowed everywhere but the brave firemen soon put it out with their powerful water hoses.
"I am so lucky to have such an exciting job," said Fireman Pete, when all was calm again. "It is wonderful to be able to help people – and cats!"

An Exciting Change

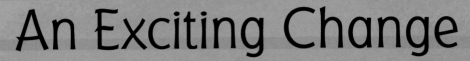

Young yellow Sporty had been on sale
for some time. "No-one wants to buy me," he said sadly,
"Do you think I am too flashy?"
"No," said red Bullet, "I think you might be too expensive
but, anyway, I am glad you are still here.
You keep me cheerful and make me laugh."
"Just enjoy the rest," said old green Banger, "Once you are out
in the real world, you'll have to work hard and drive for miles."

The very next day a great big truck arrived and Sporty was driven, slowly and carefully, up the ramp. "So, you are off at last," said Banger, "Have a wonderful time and don't forget us."
"I shall miss you so much," sobbed red Bullet.
"I'll miss you too," said Sporty but then the truck door slammed shut …
BANG! It was quite a long drive but at last the truck stopped and the door opened.

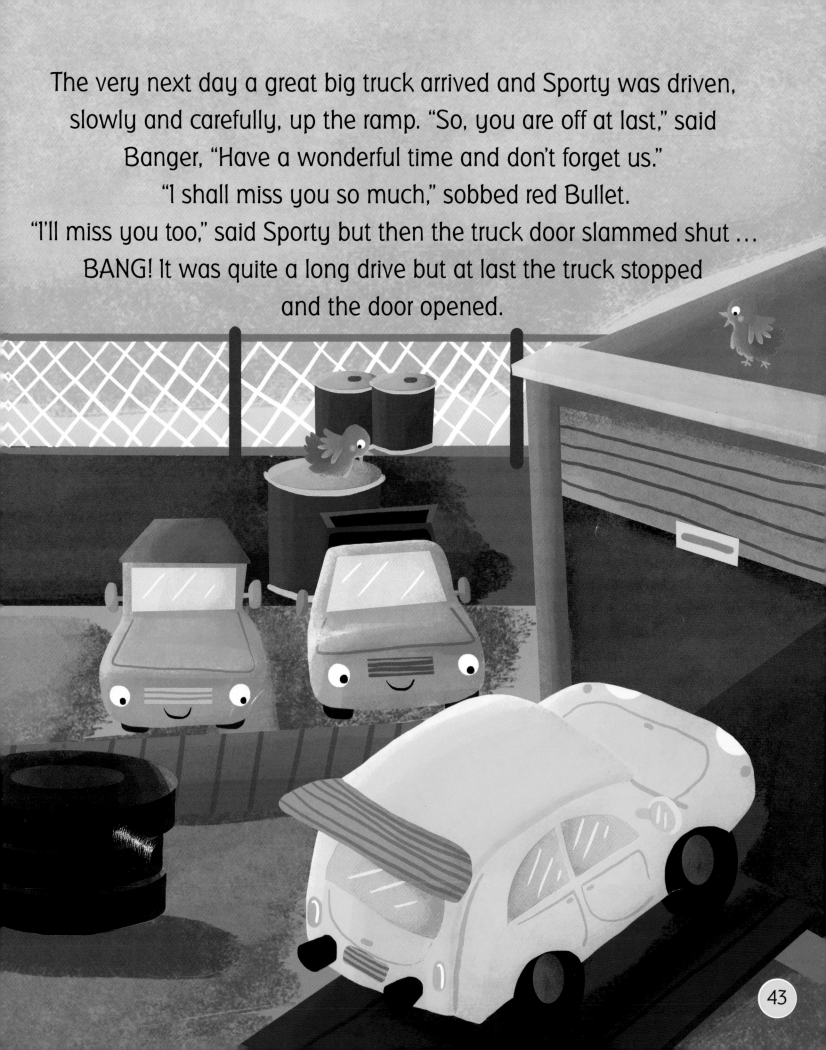

Sporty could not believe his eyes. He was by a racetrack. There were fast cars speeding along everywhere but now they all rushed over to meet him:

"Hello!"
"Hi!"
"Welcome!"
"Howdy-do!"
Sporty knew that he would miss Banger and Bullet but these young cars all seemed so friendly, he was sure he would soon settle in happily. And he was going to be a real racing car. How wonderful… How exciting! Wow!